CW00938470

Her Big Chance

A monologue from *Talking Heads*

Alan Bennett

Samuel French—London
New York-Toronto-Hollywood

ISBN 0 573 13241 0

Please see page iv for further copyright information

HER BIG CHANCE

First shown on BBC TV on 17th May 1988. The cast was as follows:

Lesley   Julie Walters

Directed by Giles Foster
Produced by Innes Lloyd
Designed by Tony Burrough

Subsequently performed at the New Grove Theatre, London, as part of the RSC Fringe Festival, opening on 30th October 1992, with the following cast:

Lesley   Kirstine Gacpar

Directed by Tim Hudson
Designed by Wendy Hodges

AUTHOR'S NOTE

The set should be kept simple. There is no point in constructing an elaborate set (still less a series of sets) and just putting one person in the middle of it all. Less, in this case, is more; the simpler the setting, the more the audience is required to use its imagination and concentrate on the performer. If you want costumes and scenery do *Carousel.*

Other plays by Alan Bennett published by
Samuel French Ltd:

Enjoy

Getting On

Habeas Corpus

Kafka's Dick (revised)

Office Suite
Green Forms *and* A Visit from Miss Prothero

The Old Country

Say Something Happened

Single Spies
An Englishman Abroad *and* A Question of Attribution

Talking Heads:
Bed Among the Lentils
A Chip in the Sugar
A Cream Cracker Under the Settee
A Lady of Letters
Soldiering On
A Woman of No Importance

HER BIG CHANCE

Lesley's flat

Music. The Lights come up

Lesley is in her thirties. It is morning and she is in her dressing-gown, though she would still be in her dressing-gown if it were afternoon

I shot a man last week. In the back. I miss it now, it was really interesting. Still. I'm not going to get depressed about it. You have to look to the future. To have something like that under your belt can be quite useful, you never know when you might be called on to repeat the experience.

It wasn't in the line of duty. I wasn't a policewoman or someone who takes violence in their stride. It was with a harpoon gun actually, but it definitely wasn't an accident. My decision to kill was arrived at only after a visible tussle with my conscience. I had to make it plain that once I'd pulled the trigger things were never going to be the same again: this was a woman at the crossroads.

It wasn't *Crossroads*, of course. They don't shoot people in *Crossroads*, at any rate not with harpoon guns. If anybody did get shot it would be with a weapon more suited to the motel ambience. I have been in *Crossroads* though, actually. I was in an episode involving a fork lunch. At least I was told it was a fork lunch, the script said it was a finger buffet. I said to the floor manager, I said, 'Rex. Are you on cans because I'd like some direction on this point.

Are we toying or are we tucking in?' He said, 'Forget it. We're losing the food anyway.' I was playing Woman in a Musquash Coat, a guest at a wedding reception, and I was scheduled just to be in that one episode. However in my performance I tried to suggest I'd taken a fancy to the hotel in the hope I might catch the director's eye and he'd have me stay on after the fork lunch for the following episode which involved a full-blown weekend. So I acted an interest in the soft furnishings, running my fingers over the formica and admiring the carpet on the walls. Only Rex came over to say that they'd put me in a musquash coat to suggest I was a sophisticated woman, could I try and look as if I was more at home in a three star motel. I wasn't at home in that sort of motel I can tell you. I said to the man I'd been put next to, whom I took to be my husband, I said, 'Curtains in orange nylon and no place mats, there's not even the veneer of civilization.' He said, 'Don't talk to me about orange nylon. I was on a jury once that sentenced Richard Attenborough to death.' We'd been told to indulge in simulated cocktail chit-chat so we weren't being unprofessional, talking. That is something I pride myself on, actually: I am professional to my fingertips.

Whatever it is I'm doing, even if it's just a walk-on, I must must must get involved, right up to the hilt. I can't help it. People who know me tell me I'm a very serious person, only it's funny, I never get to do serious parts. The parts I get offered tend to be fun-loving girls who take life as it comes and aren't afraid of a good time should the opportunity arise-type-thing. I'd call them vivacious if that didn't carry overtones of the outdoor life. In a nutshell I play the kind of girl who's very much at home on a bar stool and who seldom has to light her own cigarette. That couldn't be more different from me because for a start I'm not a smoker. I mean, I can smoke if a part requires it. I'm a professional and you need as many strings to your bow as you can in this game. But, having said that, I'm not a natural smoker and what's more I surprise my friends by not being much of a party-goer either. (Rather curl up with a book quite frankly.) *However*, this particular party I'd made an exception. Thing was I'd met this ex-graphic designer who was quitting the rat race and going off to Zimbabwe and he was having a little farewell do in the flat of an air hostess friend of his in Mitcham, would I go? I thought, well it's not every day you get somebody going off to Zimbabwe, so I said 'Yes' and I'm glad I did because that's how I got the audition.

Now my hobby is people. I collect people. So when I saw this interesting-looking man in the corner, next thing is I find myself talking to him. I said, 'You look an interesting person. I'm interested in interesting people. Hallo.' He said, 'Hallo.' I said, 'What do you do?' He said, 'I'm in films.' I said, 'Oh, that's interesting, anything in the pipeline?' He said, 'As a matter of fact, yes,' and starts telling me about this project he's involved in making videos for the overseas market, targeted chiefly on West Germany. I said, 'Are you the producer?' He said, 'No, but I'm on the production side, the name's Spud.' I said, 'Spud! That's an interesting name, mine's Lesley.' He said, 'As it happens, Lesley, we've got a problem at the moment. Our main girl has had to drop out because her back's packed in. Are you an actress?' I said, 'Well, Spud, interesting that you should ask because as a matter of fact I am.' He said, 'Will you excuse me one moment, Lesley?' I said, 'Why, Spud, where are you going?' He said, 'I'm going to go away, Lesley, and make one phone call.'

It transpires the director is seeing possible replacements the very next day, at an address in West London. Spud said, 'It's interesting because I'm based in Ealing.' I said, 'Isn't that West London?' He said, 'It is. Where's your stamping ground?' I said, 'Bromley, for my sins.' He said, 'That's a far-ish cry. Why not bed down at my place?' I said, 'Thank you, kind sir, but I didn't fall off the Christmas tree yesterday.' He said, 'Lesley, I have a son studying hotel management and a daughter with one kidney. Besides, I've got my sister-in-law staying. She's come up for the Ideal Home Exhibition.'

The penny began to drop when I saw the tattoo. My experience of tattoos is that they're generally confined to the lower echelons, and when I saw his vest it had electrician written all over it. I never even saw the sister-in-law. Still traipsing round Olympia probably.

*Music. The Lights fade, then come up again on the same setting, with
Lesley in the same dressing gown. It is afternoon. The music fades*

I know something about personality. There's a chapter about it in
this book I'm reading. It's by an American. They're the experts
where personality is concerned, the Americans; they've got it down
to a fine art. It makes a big thing of interviews so I was able to test
it out.

The director's not very old, blue suit, tie loose, sleeves turned back.
I put him down as a university type. Said his name was Simon,
which I instantly committed to memory. (That's one of the points
in the book: purpose and use of name.) He said, 'Forgive this crazy
time.' I said, 'I'm sorry, Simon?' He said, 'Like 9.30 in the
morning.' I said, 'Simon. The day begins when the day begins.
You're the director.' He said, 'Yes, well. Can you tell me what
you've done?'

I said, 'Where you may have seen me, Simon, is in *Tess*. Roman
Polanski. I played Chloë.' 'I don't remember her,' he said. 'Is she
in the book?' I said, 'Book? This is *Tess*, Simon. Roman Polanski.
Chloë was the one on the back of the farm cart wearing a shawl. The
shawl was original nineteenth-century embroidery. All hand done.
Do you know Roman, Simon?' He said, 'Not personally, no.' I said,
'Physically he's quite small but we had a very good working
relationship. Very open.' He said that was good, because Travis in
the film was very open. I said, 'Travis? That's an interesting name,
Simon.' He said, 'Yes. She's an interesting character, she spends
most of the film on the deck of a yacht.' I said, 'Yacht? That's
interesting, Simon. My brother-in-law has a small power boat
berthed at Ipswich.' He said, 'Well! Snap!' I said, 'Yes, small
world!' He said, 'In an ideal world, Lesley, I'd be happy to sit here
chatting all day but I have a pretty tight schedule and, although I
know it's only 9.30 in the morning, could I see you in your bra and
panties?' I said, '9.30 in the morning, 10.30 at night, we're both
professionals, Simon, but', I said, 'could we just put another bar on

because if we don't you won't be able to tell my tits from goose-pimples.' He had to smile. That was another of the sections in the personality book: humour, usefulness of in breaking the ice.

When I'd got my things off he said, 'Well, you've passed the physical. Now the oral. Do you play chess?' I said, 'Chess, Simon? Do you mean the musical?' He said, 'No, the game.' I said, 'As a matter of fact, Simon, I don't. Is that a problem?' He said, 'Not if you water-ski. Travis is fundamentally an outdoor girl, but we thought it might be fun to make her an intellectual on the side.' I said, 'Well, Simon, I'm very happy to learn both chess and water-skiing, but could I make a suggestion? Reading generally indicates a studious temperament and I'm a very convincing reader,' I said, 'because it's something I frequently do in real life.' I could tell he was impressed. And so I said, 'Another suggestion I could make would be to kit Travis out with some glasses. Spectacles, Simon. These days they're not unbecoming and if you put Travis in spectacles with something in paperback, that says it all.' He said, 'You've been most helpful.' I said, 'The paperback could be something about the environment or, if you want to maintain the water-skiing theme, something about water-skiing and the environment possibly. I mean, Lake Windermere.'

He was showing me out by this time but I said, 'One last thought, Simon, and that is a briefcase. Put Travis in a bikini and give her a briefcase and you get the best of every possible world.' He said, 'I'm most grateful. You've given me a lot of ideas.' I said, 'Goodbye, Simon. I hope we can work together.' The drill for saying goodbye is you take the person's hand and then put your other hand over theirs, clasp it warmly while at the same time looking into their eyes, smiling and reiterating their name. This lodges you in their mind apparently. So I did all that, only going downstairs I had another thought and I popped back. He was on the phone. 'You won't believe this,' he was saying. I said, 'Don't hang up, Simon, only I just wanted to make it crystal clear that when I said briefcase I didn't mean the old-fashioned type ones, there are new briefcases now that open up and turn into a mini writing-desk. Being an up-to-the-minute girl, that would probably be the kind of briefcase Travis would have. She could be sitting in a wet bikini with a briefcase open on her knee. I've never seen that on screen so it would be some kind of first. Ciao, Simon. Take care.'

Pause

That was last Friday. The book's got charts where you check your interview score. Mine was 75. Very good to excellent. Actually, I'm surprised they haven't telephoned.

Music. The Lights fade

Lesley changes into a different dressing gown (a wrap, perhaps; something, anyway, that is slightly smarter than the previous one) and adopts an elaborate hairstyle (a wig, probably). A canvas chair is set onstage

The Lights come up; the lighting in this scene is different from that in the previous two, to suggest we are elsewhere, though the setting is the same. It is morning

Lesley is sitting in the chair

The music fades

You'd never think this frock wasn't made for me. I said to Scott, who's Wardrobe, 'She must be my double.' He said, 'No. You're hers. The stupid cow.'

Talk about last-minute, though. Eleven o'clock on Tuesday night I'm just wondering about having a run round with the dustette, six o'clock next morning I'm sitting in Lee-on-Solent in make-up. When the phone went telling me I'd got the part I assumed it was Simon. So I said, 'Hallo, Simon.' He said, 'Try Nigel.' So I said,

'Well, Nigel, can you tell Simon that I haven't let the grass grow under my feet. I now play a rudimentary game of chess.' He said, 'I don't care if you play a championship game of ice hockey, just don't get pregnant.'

It transpires the girl they'd slated to do the part had been living with a racing driver and of course the inevitable happened, kiddy on the way. So my name was next out of the hat. I said to Scott, 'I know why. They knew I had ideas about the part.' He said, 'They knew you had a 38-inch bust.' His mother's confined to a wheelchair, he's got a lot on his plate.

Anyway, I'm ready. I've been ready since yesterday morning. It was long enough before anybody came near. I had a bacon sandwich which Scott went and fetched for me while I was under the dryer. I said, 'Wasn't there a croissant?' He said, 'In Lee-on-Solent?' On *Tess* there were croissants. On *Tess* there was filter coffee. There was also some liaison.

I wanted to talk to somebody about the part, only Scott said they were out in the speed boat doing mute shots of the coastline. On *Tess* you were never sitting around. Roman anticipated every eventuality. We filmed in the middle of a forest once and the toilet arrangements were immaculate. There was also provision for a calorie-controlled diet. I said to Scott, 'I'm not used to working like this.' He said, 'Let's face it, dear. You're not used to working. Why didn't you bring your knitting?' I said, 'I do not knit, Scott.' He said, 'Well, file your nails then, pluck an eyebrow, be like me, do something constructive.' He's as thin as a rail and apparently an accomplished pianist and he seems to be make-up as well as wardrobe. On *Tess* we had three caravans for make-up alone.

Eventually Simon puts his head round the door. I said, 'Hallo, Simon.' I said, 'Long time no see. Did Nigel tell you I've learned chess?' He said, 'Chess? Aren't you the one who can water-ski?' I said 'No.' He said 'Bugger' and disappeared. I said to Scott,

'Simon's on the young side for a director.' He said, 'Director? He couldn't direct you to the end of the street. He just does all the running about.' I said, 'Who is the director?' He said, 'Gunther.' I said, 'Gunther? That sounds a continental name.' He said, 'Yes. German.' I said, 'That's interesting. I went to Germany once. Dusseldorf.' He said, 'Well, you'll have a lot to talk about.' I've a feeling Scott may be gay. I normally like them only I think he's one of the ones it's turned bitter.

I'm still sitting there hours later when this other young fellow comes in. I said, 'Gunther?' He said, 'Nigel.' I said, 'We spoke on the phone.' He said, 'Yes. I'm about to commit suicide. I've just been told. You don't water-ski.' I said, 'Nigel. I could learn. I picked up the skateboard in five minutes.' He said, 'Precious. Five minutes is what we do not have. You don't by any chance have fluent French?' I said, 'No, why?' He said, 'They'd wondered about making her French.' I said, 'Nigel. How can she be French when she's called Travis? Travis isn't a French name.' He said, 'The name isn't important.' I said, 'It is to me. It's all I've got to build on.' He said, 'I'll get back to you.' I said, 'Nigel. I don't have French but what I do have is a smattering of Spanish, the legacy of several non-package type holidays on the Costa del Sol. Could Travis be half Spanish?' He said to Scott, 'We wanted someone with fluent French who could water-ski. What have we got? Someone with pidgin Spanish who plays chess.' Scott said, 'Well, don't tell me. I started off a landscape gardener.'

I was still waiting to be used in the afternoon which is when they did the water-skiing. Some girl from the local sub-aqua did it. She works part-time in the quayside restaurant where they all ate last night apparently. I saw her when she came in for make-up. Pleasant enough but didn't look a bit like me. I'm quite petite, only she was on the large side and whereas my hair is auburn hers was definitely ginger. I didn't say anything at the time but I thought if she's supposed to be me they'll be into big continuity problems so I thought I'd go in quest of the director and tell him. Nobody about on the yacht except a man who's dusting the camera. He said not to worry, the shot was p.o.v. water-skis so we'd only be seeing her elbow. I said, 'Will that work?' He said, 'Oh yes. You know, Cinema, the magic of.' Mind you, he said, if it was up to him personally, he'd rather see my elbow than hers any day. His name was Terry, what was mine? I said, 'It's a relief to find someone civil.' He said, 'It's the usual story, Lesley. Art comes in at the door, manners go out of the window. Why is making a film like being a mushroom?'

I said, 'Why, Terry?' He said, 'They keep you in the dark and every now and again somebody comes and throws a bucket of shit over you.' He laughed. I said, 'That's interesting, only Terry, they don't grow mushrooms like that now. It's all industrialized.' He said, 'You sound like a cultured person, what say we spend the evening exploring the delights of Lee-on-Solent?'

His room's nicer than mine. His bathroom's got a hair-dryer.

Music. The Lights fade

Lesley changes into a bikini and top, with the same wrap over them. The canvas chair is removed

The Lights come up; again, the setting is the same but is lit differently, this time to suggest a hotel room. Evening

The music fades

Please don't misunderstand me. I've no objection to taking my top off. But Travis as I was playing her wasn't the kind of girl who would take her top off. I said, 'I'm a professional, Nigel. Credit me with a little experience. It isn't Travis.'

I'd been sitting on the deck of the yacht all day as background while these two older men had what I presumed was a business discussion.

One of them, who was covered in hair and had a real weight problem, was my boyfriend apparently. You knew he was my boyfriend because at an earlier juncture you'd seen him hit me across the face. Travis is supposed to be a good-time girl, though you never actually see me having a good time, just sat on this freezing cold deck plastering on the sun tan lotion. I said to Nigel, 'I don't know whether the cameraman's spotted it, Nigel, but would I be sunbathing? There's no sun.' Nigel said, 'No sun is favourite.' Nigel's first assistant, here there and everywhere. Gunther never speaks, not to me anyway. Just stands behind the camera with a little cap on. Not a patch on Roman. Roman had a smile for everybody.

Anyway, I'm sitting there as background and I say to Nigel, 'Nigel, am I right in thinking I'm a denizen of the cocktail belt?' He said, 'Why?' a bit guardedly. I said, 'Because to me, Nigel, that implies a cigarette-holder,' and I produced quite a modest one I happened to have brought with me. He went and spoke to Gunther, only Gunther ruled there was to be no smoking. I said, 'On grounds of health?' Nigel said, 'No. On grounds of it making continuity a bugger.' I'd also brought a paperback with me just to make it easier for props (which seemed to be Scott again). Only I'd hardly got it open when Nigel relieved me of it and said they were going for the sun tan lotion. I said, 'Nigel, I don't think the two are incompatible. I can apply sun tan lotion and read at the same time. That is what professionalism means.' He checked with Gunther again and he came back and said, 'Forget the book. Sun tan lotion is favourite.' I said, 'Can I ask you something else?' He said, 'Go on.' I said, 'What is my boyfriend discussing?' He said, 'Business.' I said, 'Nigel. Would I be right in thinking it's a drugs deal?' He said, 'Does it matter?' I said 'It matters to me. It matters to Travis. It helps my character.' He said, 'What would help your character is if you took your bikini top off.' I said, 'Nigel. Would Travis do that?' I said, 'We know Travis plays chess. She also reads. Is Travis the type to go topless?' He said, 'Listen. Who do you think you're playing, Emily Brontë? Gunther wants to see your knockers.'

I didn't even look at him. I just took my top off without a word and applied sun tan lotion with all the contempt I could muster. They did the shot, then Nigel came over and said Gunther liked that and if I could give him a whisker more sensuality it might be worth a close-up. So we did it again and then Nigel came over and said Gunther was liking what I was giving them and in this next shot would I slip off my bikini bottom. I said, 'Nigel. Trust me. Travis would not do that.' Talks to Gunther. Comes back. Says Gunther agrees with me. The real Travis wouldn't. But by displaying herself naked before her boyfriend's business associate she is showing her contempt for his whole way of life. I said, 'Nigel. At last Gunther is giving me something I can relate to.' He says, 'Right! Let's shoot it! Elbow the bikini bottom!'

Pause

We wrapped about six (that's film parlance for packed up). I said to Nigel, 'Did I give Gunther what he wanted? Is he happy?' He said, 'Gunther is an artist, Lesley. He's never happy. But as he said this afternoon, "At last we're cooking with gas." I said, 'Does that mean it's good?' He said, 'Yes.' I said, 'Oh. Because I prefer electricity.'

When I got back to the hotel, it took me some time to unwind. I'd become so identified with Travis it was only when I'd had a bath and freshened up I felt her loosening her hold on me. I was looking forward to relaxing with the crew, swapping anecdotes of the day's shooting in the knowledge of a day's work well done only when I got downstairs there was nobody about, just Scott and one of the drivers. Turns out all the rest of them had gone off to supper at the restaurant run by the fat girl who did the water-skiing.

I sat in the bar for a bit. Just one fellow in there. I said, 'My hobby is people, what do you do?' Lo and behold he's on the film too, the animal handler, Kenny. In charge of the cat. I said, 'That's interesting, Kenny. I didn't know there was going to be a cat. I love cats. I love dogs too, but I love cats.' He said, 'Would you care to see her? She's asleep on my bed.' I said, 'That's convenient.' He said, 'Lesley. Don't run away with that idea. I am wedded to my small charges.' So I go up and pal on with the cat a bit and Kenny tells me about all the animals he's handled, a zebra once, a seal, an alligator and umpteen ferrets. He has a trout there too in a tank. It was going to be caught later on in the film. Quite small, only they were going to shoot it in close-up so it would look bigger.

I sat on the bed and listened to him talk about animal behaviour. I said, 'Kenny, this is the kind of evening I like, two people just talking about something interesting.'

I woke up in the night and couldn't remember where I was. Then I saw the cat sitting there, watching the trout.

Music. The Lights fade

Lesley changes back into her original dressing-gown. As you will have gathered, this is not a costume piece

The Lights come up; we are back in Lesley's flat. Dusk. The music fades

When you've finished a shot on a film you have to wait and see whether there's what they call a hair in the gate. It's film parlance for the all clear. Thank God there wasn't because I couldn't have done it again. I'd created Travis and though it was her lover that got shot I felt it was the something in me that was Travis that had died.

My lover's name turned out to be Alfredo. That was my big line. 'Alfredo!' He was the head of some sort of crime syndicate only everybody in the yachting fraternity thought he was very respectable and to do with the building trade. One night while Alfredo and me were ashore at a building federation dinner and dance this young undercover policeman swims out to the yacht to search it in his underpants. However, as luck would have it Travis has a headache,

so she and Alfredo return early from this ultra-respectable function
with Alfredo in a towering rage. Originally I was down to say, 'I
can't help it, Alfredo, I have a headache,' and we tried it once or
twice only Gunther then thought it would be more convincing if my
headache was so bad I couldn't actually speak and Alfredo just said,
'You and your headaches.' I said, 'If it's a migraine rather than a
headache Travis probably wouldn't be able to speak,' and Gunther
said, 'Whatever you say.' It's wonderful, that moment, when you
feel a director first begin to trust you and you can really start to build.

Anyway Travis and Alfredo come into the cabin where they find this
young man behind the sofa in his underpants and Alfredo takes out
his gun and says, 'How lucky lovely Travis had a headache and we
had to leave our glittering reception. I was cross with her then but
now my mood has changed. Offer the gentleman a drink, Travis.
Then go and take your clothes off. There's nothing I like better than
making love after killing a policeman. Ha ha.' I then retire to the next
cabin while Alfredo taunts this bare young policeman and says he
is going to kill him, but before he does so, he tells him about his drug-
smuggling operation in every detail, the way criminals tend to do the
minute they get somebody at gunpoint. When Travis comes back
with no clothes on the young policeman is talking about the evil
drugs do, all the young lives ruined and so on. Only I forgot to say
that there'd been some dialogue earlier, when I was supposed to be
snorkelling, about how Travis had a little brother, Craig, and how
he'd got hooked on drugs and how I was heartbroken and determined
to revenge myself on the culprits should I ever come across them.

So when the policeman is saying all this about the horror of drugs
you can see it comes as a revelation to Travis that her lover is
involved in drugs: she thinks it's just been ordinary crime and
stealing electrical goods. Anyway very quietly, 'almost pensively'
Gunther said, Travis picks up an underwater spear gun that happens
to be on the sideboard. Nigel came over and said that ideally at this
point Gunther would like to see a variety of emotions chase
themselves across Travis's face as her affection for her lover,
Alfredo, fights with the demands of her conscience and the memories

of her little brother, Craig. You see my lover's fat finger tighten on the trigger as he gets ready to shoot the policeman, only just then I say his name very quietly, 'Alfredo'. He spins round. Travis fires the harpoon and you see the spear come out of his back, killing him, and also ruining his dinner jacket. They then follow that with a big close-up with blood and everything, and me with a single tear rolling down my cheek.

We did this in one take, which Nigel said was almost unique in the annals of filming. Only Scott has to chip in and say good job, as just having one dinner jacket was fairly unique as well. I couldn't have done it again anyway. I'd got nothing left. Except I suddenly had a flash of inspiration, the way you do when you've been to the end of the world and back, and I said to Nigel, 'Don't you think that Travis, drained of all emotion by the death of her lover, would perhaps cling on to the policeman whose life she has saved, and that they would celebrate his deliverance by having sexual intercourse there and then?'

Big debate. Gunther really liked it, only the actor playing the policeman wasn't keen. I think he may have been gay too, he had a moustache. Eventually Nigel came over and said that favourite was for the policeman to look as if he was considering having sexual intercourse and for him to run his hand speculatively over Travis's private parts, only then pity drives out lust and instead he covers up her nakedness with an oriental-type dressing-gown, the property of her dead lover. Though even at this late stage you can tell he's not ruled out the possibility because as he's fastening the dressing-gown his fingers linger over Travis's nipples. Afterwards Gunther explained that if there had been any proper funny business at this point it would have detracted from the final scene when after all the excitement the undercover policeman goes home to his regular girlfriend, who cooks him a hot snack and who's a librarian, and then the final scene is of them making love, the message being that sexual intercourse is better with someone you're in love with even though they are a bit homely and work in the county library than with someone like Travis who's just after a good time. As Gunther said to me that night, 'It's a very moral film only the tragedy is, people won't see it.' I said to him, I said, 'That's interesting because I saw it that way right from the start.'

When we were in bed I said, 'If only we could have done this before.' He said, 'Lesley. I make it a rule never to lay a finger on an actress until the whole thing's in the can.' I said, 'Gunther. There's no need to explain. We're both professionals. But Gunther,' I said, 'can I ask you one question? Was I Travis? Were you pleased with my performance?' He said, 'Listen. If someone is a bad actress I can't sleep with her. So don't ask me if I was pleased with your performance. This is the proof.' He's a real artist is Gunther.

When I woke up in the morning he'd gone. I wandered down for some coffee only there was nobody from the unit about. I'd planned to say goodbye to everybody but they were off doing some establishing shots of the marina. Anyway, I went and bought a card with a sinking ship on it and put 'Goodbye, gang! See you at the première!' and left it at the desk.

As I came out with my bags Scott was just loading the laundry. I said, 'Ciao, Scott. It's been a pleasure working with you.' He said, 'You win some, you lose some.' I said, 'Now it's back to real life.' He said, 'Some of us never left it.' It's funny the way their clothes are always too small. The film's coming out in West Germany initially, then Turkey possibly. Gunther says it'll make me quite famous. Well, I suppose I shall have to live with that. Only I'm not just going to sit here and wait for the phone to ring. No fear. I'm going to acquire another skill. Spoken Italian. Selling valuable oil paintings. Canoeing. You see, the more you have to offer as a person the better you are as an actress. Acting is really just giving.

Music. The Lights fade to Black-out

FURNITURE AND PROPERTY LIST

Only the furniture indicated in the text is listed here. Further dressing may be used at the director's discretion

Off stage: Canvas chair

LIGHTING PLOT

Practical fittings required: nil
One setting, lit differently to suggest a flat, a dressing room and a hotel room

To open: General interior lighting

EFFECTS PLOT

Cue 1	As play opens *Music*	(Page 1)
Cue 2	Lights come up *Fade music*	(Page 1)
Cue 3	**Lesley**: " ... round Olympia probably." *Music*	(Page 3)
Cue 4	When ready. Lights come up *Fade music*	(Page 4)
Cue 5	**Lesley**: " ... they haven't telephoned." *Music*	(Page 6)
Cue 6	**Lesley** sits. Lights come up *Fade music*	(Page 6)
Cue 7	**Lesley**: "His bathroom's got a hair-dryer." *Music*	(Page 9)
Cue 8	**Lesley** changes; chair is removed; Lights come up *Fade music*	(Page 9)
Cue 9	**Lesley**: " ... watching the trout." *Music*	(Page 12)
Cue 10	**Lesley** changes; Lights come up *Fade music*	(Page 12)
Cue 11	**Lesley**: "Acting is really just giving." *Music*	(Page 15)